the Boys' Rainy Day book

Buster Books

Written by Ellen Bailey

Illustrated by Paul Moran

Edited by Hannah Cohen

Designed by Barbara Ward

Cover illustrated by Andrew Geeson

First published in Great Britain in 2011 by Buster Books,
an imprint of Michael O'Mara Books Limited,
9 Lion Yard, Tremadoc Road, London SW4 7NQ

A CIP catalogue record for this book is available from the British Library.

ISBN: 978-1-907151-31-6

2 4 6 8 10 9 7 5 3 1

www.mombooks.com/busterbooks

This book was printed in March 2011 at L.E.G.O., Viale dell'Industria 2, 36100, Vicenza, Italy.

Papers used by Michael O'Mara Books are natural, recyclable products made from wood grown in sustainable forests. The manufacturing processes conform to the environmental regulations of the country of origin.

CONTENTS

Haunt the house
with spooks on this stormy night.

4

PERFECT PRACTICAL PRANKS

When it's too wet to play outside, why not play these perfect pranks on members of your family instead? Here are some that are guaranteed to fool anyone and leave you in fits of giggles.

In the world of scams, the person who you play the trick on is known as a 'mark'. First, choose a mark who will find your pranking funny (and not get spooked or shout at you!), then hit him or her with these top tricks.

POOEY PRANKS

Make a fake poo by soaking a toilet-roll tube in water until it's really soggy. Next, rip it into little pieces, and then squeeze all the pieces together in the palm of your hand so that it forms a sausage-like shape.

Now position the poo somewhere that your mark is sure to find it, for instance on a chair or in a lunchbox, then hide and watch as your mark discovers it.

MAD MILK

Add a couple of drops of food dye into the milk carton before your mark wakes up in the morning – dark shades of food dye, such as blue or black work best. Then sit back and watch as your mark pours it all over his cereal. Delicious!

PENNY PLAY

To prepare for this prank, first scribble along the outside edge of a coin with a pencil. Challenge your mark to roll the coin down his nose without it falling off. After a few goes, your mark will probably give up. Then watch as your mark walks around all day long with a dark pencil line down his or her nose!

MISCHIEVOUS MIRROR

Dip your finger in vinegar and draw a spooky face on the bathroom mirror. Or write something spooky on the mirror, such as 'I'm coming to get you.' or 'I'm watching you!' When your mark has a bath or shower, the mirror will fog up but the picture or words will stay clear, giving him or her a serious case of the goose bumps.

SHOE SCAM

Stuff toilet paper into the toe-end of all your mark's shoes. Now sit back and watch your mark struggle to work out why none of his or her shoes fit anymore!

RIDE ON

If it's raining too hard to try out your tricks in the skate park, why not try out some tricky puzzle moves instead? All the answers are on page 62.

SKATER SKILLS

Check out these skaters, then answer the questions below:

A. How many skaters have backpacks on?

B. How many skaters are completely in the air?

C. How many skaters have only one arm in the air and have both feet on their skateboards?

D. How many skaters have crash-landed?

Design your own skateboard deck.

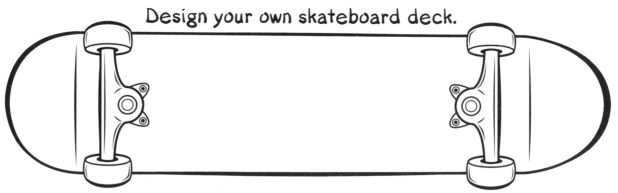

LAND THIS JUMP

Can you help skater Jim land this jump? There is only one square of paving that is safe to land on, so you need to choose very carefully where you think Jim should land so that he doesn't fall off.

Clue: The level square is white. It is in a row with three grey squares and in a column with two black squares.

CHAIN REACTION

Some skaters use chains to make sure they don't lose their wallets while they're doing tricks, but these skaters' chains have become tangled up.

Can you follow the chains to figure out which wallet belongs to which skater?

MISSION: SECRET AGENT

The Ministry of Intelligence has been watching you and thinks you might have what it takes to be its next secret agent.

All secret agents have to complete the recruitment mission below within 24 hours before being accepted by the Ministry. Each task will test a different aspect of your secret agent skills. Good luck!

SECRET AGENT SKILL 1: SECRECY

Your first task is to make your bedroom into a safe base for your secret activities. To do this, cut out a long strip of paper, and write 'Crime Scene Do Not Enter' on it. Stick it across the door to your secret base.

Next, think of a password and a secret knock. Teach these only to those people you trust to enter your secret base. Make sure no one enters your base without authorized permission for 24 hours.

SECRET AGENT SKILL 2: STEALTH

Your second task is to demonstrate your ability to disguise yourself and sneak around without being noticed. To do this, dress yourself in a disguise consisting of a hat, a pair of sunglasses and a jacket.

Next, collect each item on the list opposite from around the house, and get them back to your secret base without being noticed. If there is someone in one of the rooms you need to enter, hide behind items of furniture and carefully plan your mission so as not to be seen. You could, for example, make a loud noise or call them from another room to draw them out, and then sneak in while they're not looking.

List of items to collect:
- a towel • a ruler • a bottle of shampoo • a fork • a book
- a magazine • a bunch of keys.

SECRET AGENT SKILL 3: ATTENTION TO DETAIL

As a secret agent you will be required to give detailed and accurate information to the Ministry of Intelligence.

To demonstrate your ability to do this, cover the items you have collected in the previous task with the towel, then answer the following questions:

1. How many cm/in would you guess the length of the fork to be?

2. What brand of shampoo is it?

3. What is the title of the book?

4. How many keys are on the bunch?

5. What is on the front cover of the magazine?

Now, uncover your items and check your answers. Use the ruler to measure the length of the fork. (Your answer must be within 5 cm/2 in.) You need at least four correct answers.

SECRET AGENT SKILL 4: BRAIN POWER

All the Ministry's secret agents are given a code name. Crack the code below to find out what yours is.

Cigpv: Tckpuvqto

Clue: Move each letter two letters backwards in the alphabet.

If you can figure it out and write the correct code name in the space provided on the ID card below, you will have access to the Ministry of Intelligence. (Turn to page 62, to check that you have cracked the code correctly.)

Next, stick a photo or draw a picture of yourself in the box marked 'Photo ID'. Carefully cut out the card and keep it with you at all times.

Congratulations – you have now been accepted by the Ministry and have qualified as a secret agent.

MINISTRY OF INTELLIGENCE ID CARD

Code Name:

....

....

PHOTO ID

TOP THAT!

Make a set of personalized *Top That!* cards to play with your friends and find out which action hero wins the day.

You will need:

- 2 pieces of white A4 (8½ x 11 in) card
- scissors • a selection of pictures cut out from comics featuring cool action heroes • glue • a black pen.

1. Fold one piece of card into thirds.

2. Fold each of the thirds into thirds again to make nine small rectangles.

3. Cut along all of the folded lines.

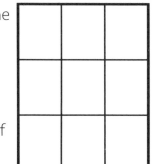

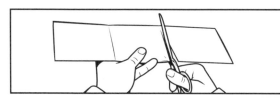

4. Repeat steps **1** to **3** on the second piece of card. You will now have 18 pieces of card.

5. In the top section of each card, either stick or draw a picture of an action hero, such as Superman, Spiderman or Batman.

6. Write down the following categories under each picture:

Intelligence:
Strength:
Speed:
Fighting Skills:

BACK OF SECRET AGENT ID CARD

7. Score each action hero on each of the categories to complete the cards.

For example, Superman might score 10 on Strength and only 5 on Speed – it's up to you.

Top Tip. Make sure you include at least one high score and at least one low score on each card.

HOW TO PLAY

You will need two or more players to play this game.

1. First shuffle the cards, then deal all of them out to the players, placing them face down on top of each other.

2. Each player must pick up all their cards and hold them, so they can see the top card only.

3. The player to the left of the dealer, Player A, starts by reading out one of their categories and the score on their card, such as, 'Fighting Skills: 8'.

4. The other players then take it in turns to read out the score for the same category on their top card.

5. The player who reads out the highest score wins the top card from each player in the round.

• If two or more players share the highest score for the category, all the cards from that round are placed in the middle and Player A chooses another category from his next card.

• The winner of the round wins all the cards from the middle as well as the cards in play.

6. The winning player must then put his winning card to the bottom of his pile of cards, and pick a category to play from his new top card.

The player with all the cards at the end is the winner.

UNBELIEVABLE WEATHER

Extreme weather can be pretty unbelievable sometimes, but which of the wacky weather facts below isn't true? The answer is revealed on page 62.

FACT 1. Most hailstones (lumps of ice that fall like rain during storms) are smaller than 2.5 cm (1 in) in diameter, but some are as big as grapefruits.

FACT 2. Tornadoes (funnels of spinning air) can travel over 200 kilometres (124 miles), and pick up cats, dogs, cows and even cars!

FACT 3. Raindrops are not 'teardrop' shape at all. They are more or less spherical as they fall.

FACT 4. A tornado out at sea can pick up fish, frogs and other animals. As it moves inland, they are dropped to the ground with the rain. In March 1998, it apparently rained frogs in Croydon, England.

FACT 5. In 1930, it was reported that during a severe hailstorm in the USA, a turtle entirely frozen in ice fell to Earth with the hail.

FACT 6. At all times, there are approximately 2,000 thunderstorms occurring in the Earth's atmosphere.

FACT 7. In 2009, Sydney, Australia turned red when a dust storm hit the city. The red dust created a huge cloud that hid buildings and disrupted flights.

FACT 8. All snow crystals are hexagonal (this means they have six sides) and are identical in shape and size.

FACT 9. In 2010, in South Dakota, USA, a hailstone fell that measured 20 cm (8 in) across – that's nearly the size a volleyball.

FACT 10. Roy Sullivan, a park ranger in Virginia, USA, was struck by lightning seven times, on separate occasions – and survived! He suffered injuries to his arms, chest, stomach and legs, lost his eyebrows and a toenail, and even had his hair set on fire.

PEN WARFARE

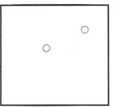

To play this strategy game of Pen Warfare, you will need a piece of paper, a pencil, a pen, and an opponent with a different pen. Follow the instructions below to find out how to win the war.

To begin the game, draw two dots anywhere on the piece of paper using the pencil.

Next, take it in turns to follow steps **1** and **2** to make a move, following the rules below:

1. Use your pen to draw a curve to join two dots or join a single dot to itself.

2. Draw a new dot somewhere along the curve, as shown here.

PEN WARFARE RULES

- No more than three lines can come out of each dot.
- Do not pass over another curve.
- Do not pass over another dot.

THE AIM

To trap your opponent so that they are not able to make a move.

The last player to be able to move wins the war.

In the example below, the light pen army wins after five rounds because the dark pen army cannot make a move.

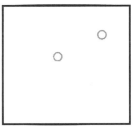

(DOTS MARKING BATTLEGROUND BEFORE PLAY COMMENCES.)

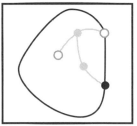

(LIGHT PEN ARMY MOVE.)

(DARK PEN ARMY MOVE.)

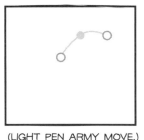

(LIGHT PEN ARMY MOVE.)

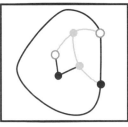

(DARK PEN ARMY MOVE.)

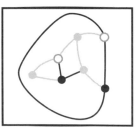

(WINNING LIGHT PEN ARMY MOVE.)

REACH INTO A MONSTER'S STOMACH

... if you dare! First, make the monster below, then challenge members of your family to reach into his stomach to guess what he has eaten.

To make the monster, you will need:

• some old newspaper • a large cardboard box • a large piece of card • a pencil • scissors • paints • glue.

1. Draw a monster's face on to the piece of card. The monster should have a large open mouth with big teeth.

2. Cut out a circle inside the monster's mouth so that there is a hole big enough to fit your hand inside.

3. Carefully cut around the outline of the head.

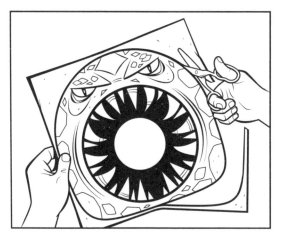

4. Lay the newspaper down on a table, then paint your monster, making him as scary-looking as possible. Leave to dry completely.

5. Carefully, cut a hole that is as big as your monster's mouth on one side of the box.

6. Glue the monster face to the side of the box so that the monster's mouth is directly over the hole. Paint the outside of the box and leave to dry.

HOW TO PLAY

• Each player must choose three different items that will feel gross to touch from around the house, for example, peeled grapes, a slimy bar of soap or cubes of jelly work well.

• Take it in turns to place items in the box and challenge the other players to reach into the monster's stomach.

• Each player then has to guess what the monster has had for his dinner, using only one hand. The player who guesses the most items correctly wins.

MOUNTAIN OF DOOM

The monster that lives on the Mountain of Doom has been terrifying the town. Can you find your way through the mountain to defeat him at the other end?

Be warned – if your path is blocked by venomous snakes, you cannot pass. You must pass over only one pack of dynamite and one flame thrower on your way. Turn to page 62 for help if you get lost. Quick, he's waking up!

15

BUILD A COOL CAMP

Be the King of the Castle and make the coolest camp out of stuff you can find lying around the house.

RECONNAISSANCE MISSION

Identify a table or a desk to form the 'anchor' – the basic structure – for your cool camp.

BUILDING WORK

Position chairs all around the anchor, then tie scarves from the tops of the chairs to the top joints of your anchor, as shown below. The scarves act as the support beams for the camp.

Position large cushions around the chairs to build up the walls, then drape sheets and blankets over the entire camp structure.

FAKE ENTRANCE

Fool intruders by making a fake entrance to your camp. On one side of the camp, place a few large cardboard boxes in two rows, leaving a gap large enough for a person to crawl through in between the rows.

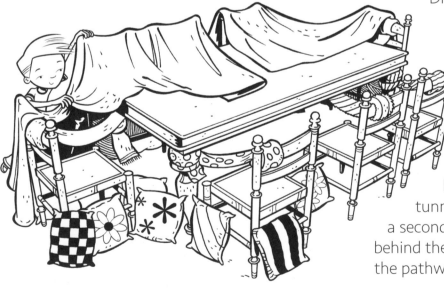

Drape a sheet over the boxes as shown above, and pin the ends of this sheet underneath the corners of the boxes closest to your camp. This will create a 'sheet wall' between the fake tunnel and your camp. Pile a second wall of cushions behind the sheet wall to block the pathway of an intruder.

Place a sign saying 'Entrance Tunnel' in front of the fake tunnel.

Now, make a real entrance on the other side of your camp by simply removing a wall of cushions to make a space between two chairs big enough to crawl through. Make sure no one sees you using the real entrance.

SOFT-TOY CANNONBALLS LAUNCH AREA

Find as many soft toys as you can and bring them into the fort. If you hear someone breaking their way through the tunnel, launch the soft toys at the enemy until he or she retreats.

Make sure there is also an area between the chairs on each side of your camp where you can fold back the sheets and blankets to create a hole big enough to throw soft toy cannonballs at intruders breaking in on any side.

STICKY TRAPS

Further secure your fort by placing booby traps along the tunnel. To do this, crawl half way along the tunnel and lie on your back. Stick strips of sticky tape to dangle from the sheet roof of the tunnel so that the sticky side will hit intruders in the face.

ACQUIRE SUPPLIES

Kit out your camp with the following special equipment:

- sleeping bags
- pillows and comfy cushions
- warm blankets
- a torch
- sticky tape (for re-setting booby traps)
- a notebook and pens
- binoculars
- cool stuff, for example your skateboard, books and magazines
- snacks and drinks
- a dustpan and brush for keeping your camp clean of crumbs.

Now, kick back and enjoy being the King of your Castle! Remember to keep your eyes and ears open for intruders.

SPORTS-QUIZ SHOWDOWN

Get your brain in training with
these seriously sporting quiz questions.

1. Mark a cross in the medals below that you think show an Olympic sport, and leave blank the ones that you think haven't made it into the games.

FOOTBALL — EXTREME IRONING — BOXING — WEIGHT-LIFTING — BOG SNORKELLING — ROWING

2. Draw a line to connect each animal with the correct competition:

Camel   Running (Spain)

Bull   Derby (USA)

Duck   Wrestling (Turkey)

Hot Dog   Polo (Nepal)

Elephant   Eating (USA)

3. Draw a line to connect the terms below to their sports:

Love, Deuce   Cricket

Salute, Parry   Ten-Pin Bowling

Birdie, Eagle   Fencing

Skittle, Strike   Golf

Duck, Boundary   Tennis

4. Why was boxer Daniel Caruso unable to fight in 'The Golden Gloves Championships' in 1992?

A. He forgot to turn up.

B. He had a broken nose from punching himself in the face.

C. He overslept.

D. He was grounded.

5. How many ways are there of getting 'out' in cricket?

A. Seven.

B. One.

C. Ten.

D. Thirty.

6. The Olympic motto is 'Citius, Altius, Fortius'. What does it mean?

A. Swifter, Higher, Stronger.

B. Hop, Skip, Jump.

C. Sports, Games, Fun.

D. Stamina, Strength, Speed.

7. What do archers store their arrows in?

A. A quiver.

B. A snake.

C. A rucksack.

D. A water bottle.

8. Which of the following is NOT a pro-wrestling move?

A. Mongolian Chop.

B. Irish Whip.

C. Russian Legsweep.

D. Egyptian Breaker.

9. Which of the following is a Japanese style of fencing?

A. Kite Flying.

B. Kendo.

C. Kick Start.

D. Kung Fu.

Check your answers on page 62 and then, starting at the bottom, shade in a step up the podiums for each correct answer that you scored. There are a possible 20 right answers in total, so if you get every one right you will have made it to the gold medal!

GOLD — Congratulations — you have won Gold!

20.
19.
18.
17.
16.
15.
14.
13.

SILVER — Proceed to the bottom of the Gold podium.

12.
11.
10.
9.
8.
7.
6.

BRONZE — Proceed to the bottom of the Silver podium.

5.
4.
3.
2.
1. **START HERE**

TREASURE TACTICS

Avoid sinking sand and life-sucking ghost pirates to find the treasure and beat your opponent back to base before turning into an old man.
You will need an opponent, a pen and four pieces of paper.

1. Trace the island map grid below on to four pieces of paper.

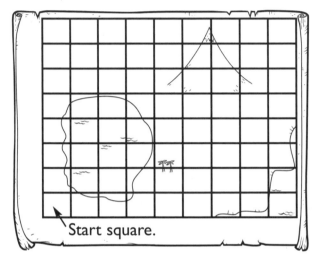

Start square.

2. Give two maps to your opponent and keep two for yourself. One of your maps is called a 'tracking map', and the other is an 'object map'.

3. Each player must then hide the items listed below on his object map by placing the corresponding letters in the squares of the grid:

3 x Sinking sand (**S**), 3 x Pirate ghost (**P**), 1 x Fountain of youth (**F**), 1 x Treasure chest (**T**).

Make sure your opponent doesn't see where you place the objects on your map.

4. Each player must draw three boxes in a row underneath one map to be a 'youthometer chart', which shows how many lives you have left.

5. The youngest player (Player 1) begins in the Start square on his tracking map and moves by describing his pathway.

For example, he might say, 'I'm moving up four squares.' You can move up and down and left and right, but not diagonally.

6. Player 2 follows Player 1's route on his object map, and tells Player 1 if he passes through a square containing an object. If so, Player 1 stops moving and follows the instructions for that object below:

Sinking sand = Miss a turn.

Pirate ghost = They suck your life away, turning you into an old man. Mark a cross in your youthometer chart. If you get hit three times, you die and lose the game.

Fountain of Youth = Drinking from this will restore you and wipe the crosses from your youthometer chart.

7. Take turns to make a move. The first player to find the treasure and return to the Start square wins.

Design a superhero outfit to conceal your true identity.
Now turn the page to help save the day before
Nasty Nemesis and his Ugly Crew cause havoc.

CAN YOU SAVE THE DAY?

Help! Nasty Nemesis and his Ugly Crew have stolen gold from the bank. A superhero is needed to solve the problems and save the day. Have you got what it takes? Tackle these puzzles to find out, then check your answers on page 63.

ON THE RUN

Follow the movements of the Ugly Crew to see where they ended up.

They came out of the bank and turned right. They took a left at the corner, then took the first left down a street. They turned right at the corner, then left at the next corner.

They took the third road to the right, then turned right. They then turned right again into a house. Did they run into house A, B or C?

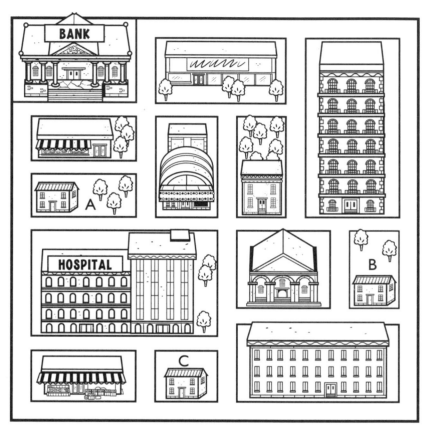

CODE CRACKER

By the time you arrive at the house, the gang has gone, but you find a safe and the gold's inside. Can you crack the code to find the secret combination that will open the safe? (**Clue:** Nasty Nemesis isn't very smart and has used his own name to lock it.)

A	B	C	D	E	F	G	H	I	J	K	L	M
1	2	3	4	5	6	7	8	9	10	11	12	13
N	O	P	Q	R	S	T	U	V	W	X	Y	Z
14	15	16	17	18	19	20	21	22	23	24	25	26

TREASURE TRICKS

Inside the safe you find half the stolen gold and a piece of paper with the numbers below on it. Can you crack the code to find out where the rest of the gold is hidden? (**Clue:** Each number represents a letter of the alphabet.)

2, 21, 18, 9, 5, 4 / 21 ,14, 4, 5, 18 / 20, 18, 5, 5 / 14, 5, 24, 20 / 20, 15 / 8, 15, 19, 16, 9, 20, 1, 12

MATCH THE PRINT

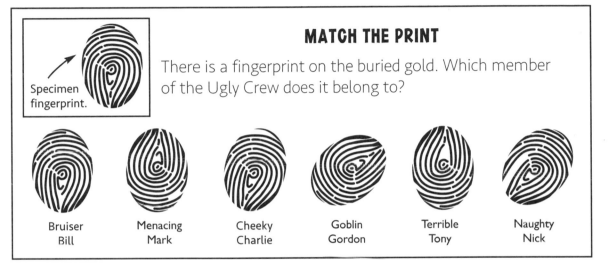

There is a fingerprint on the buried gold. Which member of the Ugly Crew does it belong to?

Specimen fingerprint.

Bruiser Bill | Menacing Mark | Cheeky Charlie | Goblin Gordon | Terrible Tony | Naughty Nick

PRISON CELLS

You have captured three members of the Ugly Crew and thrown them into prison. The guards have asked you to keep a close eye on them in case they try to escape. Can you write down the co-ordinates (the letter of the column and the number of the row) of the three squares that have their prison numbers inside?

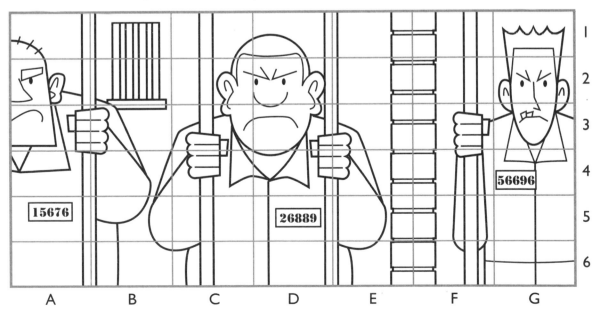

WATER FIGHT!

It wasn't long before the boys' water fight landed them in seriously hot water ... read on, to find out how they escaped the clutches of the grumpy lock keeper.

'Wooohooo! School's closed because the roof is leaking!' yelled James to his brother. 'Get your wellies on, Rob, it's time for a water fight.'

'But it's pouring with rain!' Rob groaned. James could always think of a way to have a fight – snowball fights, freshly-cut grass fights, sock fights – the list was endless. James was two years older than Rob, and Rob always ended up with grass down his pants or snow in his socks.

'It's even more fun when it's raining. I'll let you have the Hydro-Blaster,' James promised. The Hydro-Blaster – an extremely powerful water pistol – was one of James's most treasured possessions. It was impossible for Rob to resist.

The boys pulled on their raincoats and wellies. James headed outside while Rob went to fill the giant water pistol.

Armed with a pistol full of water, Rob opened the front door and stepped out into the street. It was raining so hard that it was like stepping under a shower that was on full blast.

Splash! Suddenly, James jumped out from behind a wall and kicked a giant puddle at Rob. Rob was soaked. 'Bet you can't catch me,' laughed James, as he raced off down the street.

Rob wiped his eyes and ran after his brother. Rob kept trying to shoot James but his brother was too fast and too good at dodging the stream of water. When James disappeared from sight, Rob shut his eyes and braced himself for another puddle attack. He opened his eyes again, but James was nowhere to be seen.

'James, where are you?' Rob had a feeling something was wrong. 'It's not funny ...' he shouted. Rob turned the corner and saw the river – it was twice its normal size. He spotted something red caught on a branch. Could that be ...? Yes, that most definitely was James's anorak. Rob's stomach flipped over. Had James been swept into the river?

Rob ran as fast as he could downstream to the part of the river where the lock keeper lived. He felt a shiver run down his spine, and it wasn't because he was cold.

The lock keeper had a small house on the other side of the river, and was responsible for allowing boats to pass through the lock. He had a reputation in the village for having a nasty temper, and he disliked little boys playing near his house. James and Rob were always too terrified to come down to this part of the river.

'Help me!' Rob spun his head round just in time to see the lock keeper pulling James along by his arm. James was wriggling to get free.

Rob ran to the bank and shouted, 'Excuse me! That's my brother and I've come to take him home.' The lock keeper raised an eyebrow. 'I found your brother hiding down by the water's edge – he could have been swept away. I'm taking him in so I can tell the police I have a troublemaker for them.'

Just as he got to his front door, the lock keeper noticed Rob's Hydro-Blaster out of the corner of his eye. 'That looks like a very powerful water pistol ... how far does it shoot?' he asked.

'I'm not sure, pretty far!' Rob replied.

The lock keeper thought for a moment, then roared, 'I challenge you to a water fight! If you win, I won't call the police about your brother. Give me your pistol!'

Before Rob could reply, the lock keeper snatched James's pistol from his hands and fired. Rob instantly felt the cold water trickling down his neck. He fought back hard, and in the pouring rain the lock keeper found it difficult to dodge the Hydro-Blaster's shots.

Finally, the lock keeper yelled out, 'Stop! I surrender!', roaring with laughter. 'That was the most fun I've had in years! You can have your brother back, but if I find either of you playing by the river again, there'll be trouble!'

A relieved Rob piped up, 'Don't worry, we won't. If you ever fancy another water fight though ....' The lock keeper smiled, 'I might just take you up on that offer!'

WHAT'S YOUR ULTIMATE SUPER POWER?

Which is better? Being invisible or having x-ray vision? Being able to predict the future or having laser eyes? Decide for yourself with this super-duper super-power decider!

1. Think of four super powers that you would love to have and write one inside each of the fireballs on the first row.

2. Decide which of each pair you think would be the most fun to have and write the answers in the fireballs on the second row.

3. Finally, decide which of these two would be your ultimate super power and write it in the fireball on the last row.

ULTIMATE SUPER POWER

26

Cover the rocks with creepy-crawlies.

MAKE A MAGGOT HAND

Create a maggot-infested rotting hand that will seriously freak out your friends and family.

You will need:

• a handful of white jelly sweets (such as milk bottles) • a packet of lime jelly (Jell-O)• a thin rubber or latex glove • a rubber band • scissors.

1. Carefully use a knife to carefully cut the jelly sweets into small maggot-sized rectangles.

2. Next, follow the instructions on the packet to make up the jelly. Stir in the maggot sweets.

3. Rinse out the glove thoroughly with warm water, even though you are not going to eat your maggot hand.

4. Carefully pour the jelly mix into the glove. Tie a knot in the top, and place it in the freezer overnight.

5. The next day, remove the glove from the freezer.

6. Carefully use a pair of scissors to cut through the glove and peel it off the jelly, to reveal a whole jelly hand.

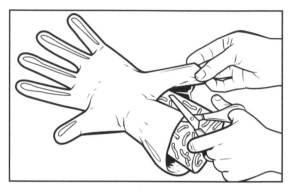

7. Place the hand somewhere where it will be spotted easily – why not rest it on a shelf in the fridge, or leave it in the bathroom cabinet? Gross!

GO-KART GO!

To complete this go-kart race, each driver must race to the flag that matches the one on his go-kart. Drivers can drive straight up, down and sideways, but not diagonally across the squares. Only one go-kart can pass through each square. Can you find a route for each go-kart? The first one has been done for you. Turn to page 63 if you get stuck.
On your marks, get set, go!

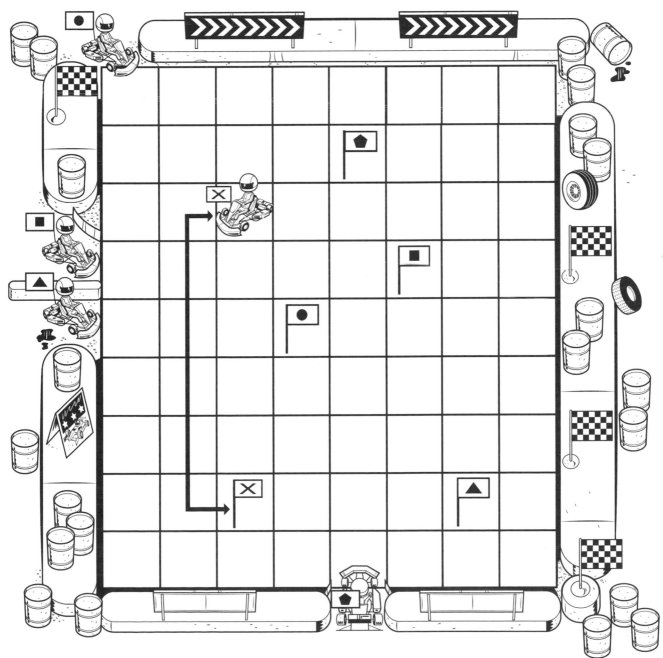

BE A MATHEMATICAL MASTERMIND

Use mathematics to read your friends' minds, impress your parents or teachers with lightning-speed calculations and even guess their age using the power of sums! You don't need to be a genius to be a mathematical mastermind, you just need to know these tricks.

MIND READER

Give a friend the following instructions:

1. 'Choose a number – any number.'

2. 'Double it.'

3. 'Add ten.'

4. 'Divide it by two.'

5. 'Subtract your original number from the new one.'

Then place your hands on your friend's head and close your eyes as if you are reading his mind. The secret of this trick is that the answer is always five! He will be amazed when you guess correctly the number he was thinking of.

THE MAGIC NUMBER

For this trick you will need a pen and five pieces of paper.

• On the first piece of paper, write the following numbers:

1, 3, 5, 7, 9, 11, 13, 15, 17, 19, 21, 23, 25, 27, 29, 31

• On the second piece, write the following numbers:

2, 3, 6, 7, 10, 11, 14, 15, 18, 19, 22, 23, 26, 27, 30, 31

• On the third piece, write the following numbers:

4, 5, 6, 7, 12, 13, 14, 15, 20, 21, 22, 23, 28, 29, 30, 31

• On the fourth piece, write the following numbers:

8, 9, 10, 11, 12, 13, 14, 15, 24, 25, 26, 27, 28, 29, 30, 31

• On the fifth piece, write the following numbers:

16, 17, 18, 19, 20, 21, 22, 23, 24, 25, 26, 27, 28, 29, 30, 31

You are now ready to start the trick. First, lay out the five pieces of paper on a table. Ask a friend to think of a number between 1 and 31.

Next, ask him to point to each piece of paper that has their number on it.

To find the correct number, simply add together the smallest number on each piece of paper that is pointed to.

For example, if his number was 11, he would point to the first, second and fourth pieces of paper.

The smallest numbers on each of those are 1, 2 and 8. 1 + 2 + 8 = 11, which is the number that he was thinking of.

GUESS SOMEONE'S AGE

Claim that you can guess anyone's age with the power of calculation. Simply ask the questions below to find out how. This trick only works if the person is ten or over. (Watch out for sneaky people lying about their age, too!)

1. Ask the person to multiply the first number of his or her age by five.

2. Ask him or her to add three to this figure.

3. Ask him or her to double it.

4. Ask the person to add the second number of his or her age to this figure. Ask him or her to tell you this number.

5. Take six away from the number that he or she has told you in step **4.** The number you end up with, should be the person's age.

43×68+9÷214+73×2÷

Lightning-Speed Calculation

There's a quick way to check if a number can be divided exactly by three. Simply add up all the digits, and if they come to 3, 6 or 9, the number can be divided by three.

For 81, 8+1=9, so 81 can be divided by three. For 43, 4+3=7, which means 43 can't be divided by three.

The trick even works for huge numbers such as, 22,358,892. 2+2+3+5+8+8+9+2=39, 3+9=12, 1+2=3, so 22,358,892 can be divided by three.

GRAN ... 27?

FLY TRAP

Follow the cobweb lines to work out which spider has trapped which fly.
The answer is on page 63.

RAIN-DANCE DIFFERENCES

Some cultures believe that a ritual called a 'rain dance' makes the rains come, helping their crops to grow. There are 15 differences between these two pictures of boys performing a rain dance. Can you spot them all? The answer is on page 63.

PAPER CATAPULT FUN

Find out how to make your very own paper catapult, then have fun firing paper-ball missiles at unsuspecting passers-by!

You will need:

- 2 A4 (8½ x 11 in) pieces of paper.

1. Cut out a square of paper roughly 21 cm x 21 cm (8 in x 8 in).

2. Position the square of paper on a flat surface, so that one of the corners is pointing towards you.

3. Fold the piece of paper in half from corner to corner, then unfold it again.

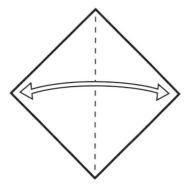

4. Fold in the bottom left and right corners of the square so that they meet with the crease in the middle. You should now have a kite-shape.

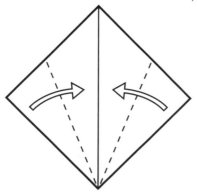

5. Fold the sides of the kite-shape into the middle again so that they meet with the crease in the middle.

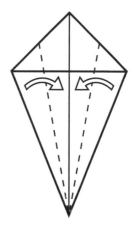

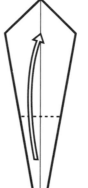

6. Turn the shape over.

7. Fold the point at the bottom of the kite-shape up to meet the point at the top.

This will be your triangular handle.

8. Pick up the right-hand edge of the triangular handle you have just made and push the bottom-right corner of it in between the two layers of paper so that it meets the crease in the middle, as shown here.

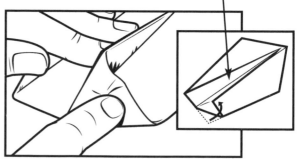

Triangular handle.

9. Do the same with the bottom-left corner. It should now look like this:

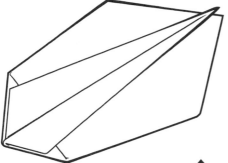

10. Pick up the right-hand edge of the triangular handle and fold it into the central fold, as shown here.

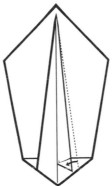

11. Pick up the left-hand edge of the triangular handle and fold it into the centre fold.

12. Fold the top point of the triangle arm back down, as shown here. Your catapult is ready to fire. Read on to find out how.

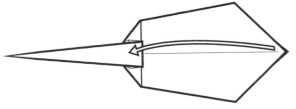

TAKE AIM AND FIRE

1. Make a pile of paper catapult balls by tearing off small strips from the other piece of paper and screwing each strip up into tight balls.

2. Hold your catapult by gripping the triangle handle in your right fist, with your right thumb pinning the edge of the catapult to the triangle arm.

The index finger on your other hand should be holding the top of the catapult. Place a catapult ball here.

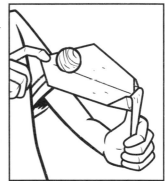

3. Pull the top of the catapult back as far as it will go, then take aim and let go of the top of the catapult. Your paper missile should launch into the air. Keep launching missiles until you can hit a designated target.

RACE TO DEFEAT THE DRAGON

A dragon has been terrorizing the country, and the King has offered a reward of one million gold coins to the warrior who can defeat it. Race your friends through the dragon's lair and be the first to creep up on the sleeping dragon to win the prize.

To get started, each player places a coin in the start box. Take it in turns to spin the spinner (follow the instructions opposite to find out how) and move forward the number of spaces shown. Good luck!

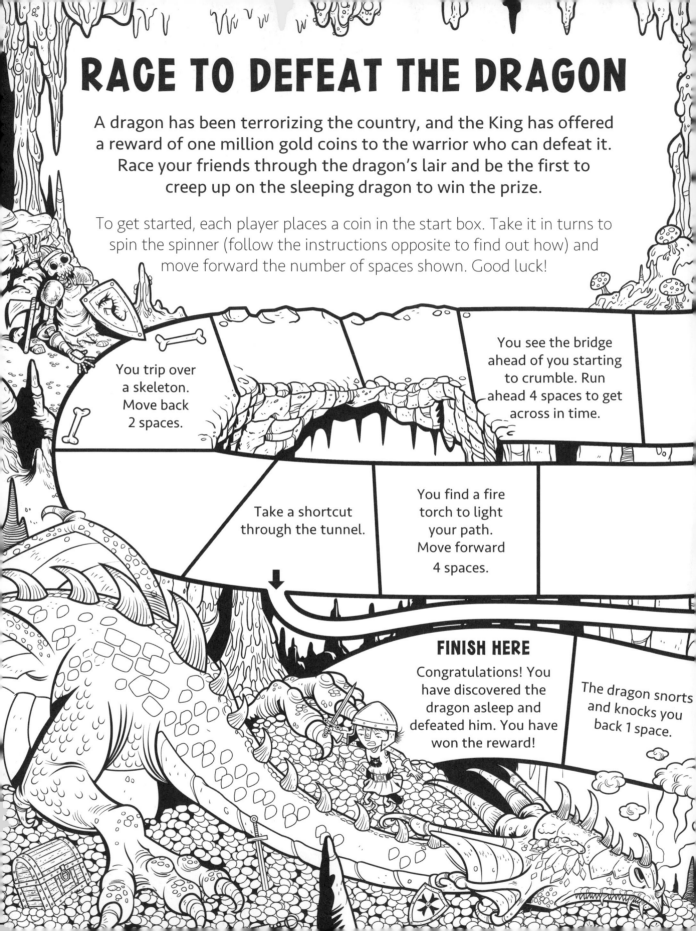

You trip over a skeleton. Move back 2 spaces.

You see the bridge ahead of you starting to crumble. Run ahead 4 spaces to get across in time.

Take a shortcut through the tunnel.

You find a fire torch to light your path. Move forward 4 spaces.

FINISH HERE

Congratulations! You have discovered the dragon asleep and defeated him. You have won the reward!

The dragon snorts and knocks you back 1 space.

START HERE

You get splashed by an eruption of lava. Miss a go.

You stop to sharpen your sword. Miss a go.

You find a map on an old scroll. Spin again.

You fall through a trap door. Miss a go.

A colony of bats attacks. Move back 4 spaces.

You follow some rats in the right direction. Move forward 2 spaces.

Cut out the spinner and pierce the middle with a toothpick. Hold the tip of the toothpick on a flat surface and spin it between your thumb and forefinger. When it stops spinning, the number at the top of the spinner is the number of spaces you should move your coin.

SAFARI SPOT

Imagine you're far away on safari on the African plains. Write down how many of each animal you can spot in the boxes on the guidebook below. All the answers are on page 63.

BACK OF SPINNER

GUIDEBOOK

Giraffe
Rhino
Lion
Zebra
Cheetah
Elephant
Warthog

PICTURE THIS

Below is a picture of a medieval knight on horseback. Using the squares below to help you, can you copy it?

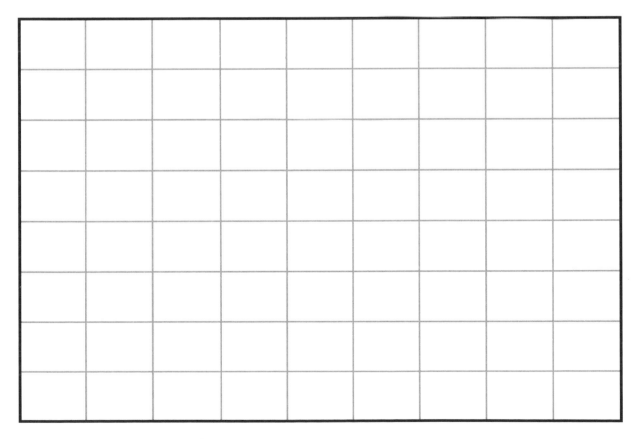

FLY A UFO

Unidentified Flying Objects, commonly known as UFOs, are one of the world's great mysteries. Some people believe these flying saucers could be alien aircraft. Find out how to make your own, then send it flying through the solar system on a cool alien adventure.

MAKE A UFO

You will need:

- an old Frisbee • a tennis ball
- silver duct tape • a black marker pen
- a large bowl • 8 pieces of
A3 (11½ x 16½ in) paper.

1. Place the tennis ball in the middle of the top of the Frisbee and use a couple of strips of duct tape to hold it in place.

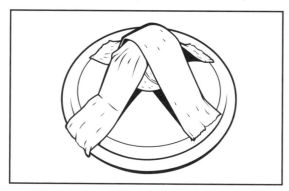

2. Continue wrapping strips of duct tape over the tennis ball and around the Frisbee until it is covered.

3. Use the marker pen to draw windows around the tennis ball part of your UFO.

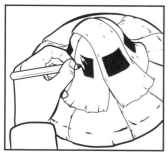

4. Throw your UFO as you would a Frisbee until you get the hang of it.

MAKE THE SOLAR SYSTEM

5. Draw around the bowl to create a circle on each piece of paper – these will represent the eight planets of the solar system.

6. Cut each circle out.

7. Write the name of a different planet in the solar system inside each circle.

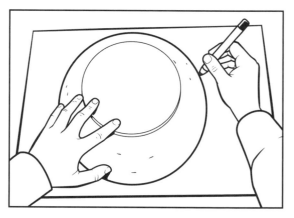

The names of the planets in the solar system are:

Mercury, Venus, Earth, Mars, Jupiter, Saturn, Uranus and Neptune.

8. Arrange your planet circles in the above order in a line on the floor. Mercury is closest to the sun.

ALIEN GAME PLAY

You're now ready to launch your UFO into space and begin your alien adventure.

Your Mission: You have been informed by the head aliens on the mother ship that your UFO must land on each of the planets of the solar system in order.

Place the bowl at the bottom of the line of planets (this represents the Sun) and stand with one leg on either side of the bowl.

Now throw the UFO so that it lands on Mercury.

If you're successful, retrieve the UFO and then throw it so that it lands on Venus. If you are unsuccessful, you must start again at Mercury.

Continue until you have visited each of the planets, always starting again at Mercury and visiting the planets in order if any of your throws are unsuccessful.

Why not time yourself to see how quickly you can complete your flight through the solar system? Good luck, alien explorer.

The Sun.

DID YOU KNOW?

For 76 years, Pluto was considered the ninth and smallest planet in the solar system. It lost its planet status in 2006 however, when it was re-classified as a 'dwarf planet' because it was considered too small to be a proper planet.

MERCURY

VENUS

EARTH

MARS

JUPITER

SATURN

URANUS

NEPTUNE

COOL KITCHEN SCIENCE

Torrential rain, thunder and lightning are the perfect backdrop for a mad scientist to conduct his experiments. So when the weather is wild, why not turn your kitchen into your very own laboratory and carry out your own scientific observations?

ERUPTION EQUATION

This chemical equation might not look like much fun, but the result is an eruption of volcanic proportions.

$$NaHCO_3 + CH_3COOH = CO_2 + H_2O + CH_3COONa$$

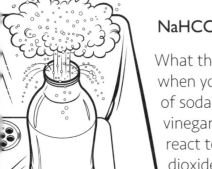

What this means is that when you mix bicarbonate of soda ($NaHCO_3$) with vinegar (CH_3COOH) they react to form carbon dioxide (CO_2) plus water (H_2O) plus sodium acetate (CH_3COONa).

To try it out yourself, put a small, empty plastic bottle in the sink. Use a funnel to pour a cup of bicarbonate of soda into the bottle. Mix a squirt of washing-up liquid into a cup full of vinegar, then pour this into the bottle of bicarbonate of soda. Stand well back as your chemical equation erupts!

FREAKY FOOD PLAY

Scientists have proved that the human brain associates how a food looks and smells with how it will taste. For example, if a berry is red and smells sweet your brain assumes it will be ripe and taste delicious, or if a piece of meat is green, it will be bad. To test this theory, you will need a volunteer.

Experiment 1. Ask your volunteer to put on a blindfold and give him a piece of white bread to eat. While he eats it, hold some vanilla essence near his nose, then hide it before he takes his blindfold off. Now ask him what he has just eaten.

Experiment 2. Ask your volunteer to leave the room, then pour three glasses of lemonade and put a drop of red food dye in the first glass, a drop of blue in the second, and a drop of green in the third. Now ask him to try each of the three drinks and guess what flavours they are.

Be prepared to be freaked out by your findings!

TAKE THE CABBAGE TEST

This experiment uses cabbage to test if a liquid is acid or alkali. Really strong acids can eat through metal, but acids such as lemon juice are relatively weak. Alkalis are the opposite of acids and some, such as bicarbonate of soda, can be used for cleaning. Discover whether something is acid or alkali yourself with this cool testing-kit.

You will need:

• half a red cabbage • several empty glass jars • a variety of liquids to test, such as lemon juice, vinegar, cola and washing-up liquid • a variety of solids to test, such as bicarbonate of soda or toothpaste.

1. Dissolve a teaspoon of each solid in some water. Pour each dissolved solid into a separate jar and label each jar with the name of the dissolved solid inside it.

2. Pour each liquid into a separate jars. Label each jar with the name of the liquid inside it.

3. Chop the cabbage into small pieces, put it into a saucepan and cover it with water from the tap.

4. Ask an adult to help you bring the water to the boil, then turn down the heat, so that the water simmers (bubbles gently) for 20 minutes.

5. Ask an adult to help you strain the purple cabbage water into a jug. This is your testing liquid. Leave it to cool completely.

6. Line up your testing jars. Pour a small amount of testing liquid into the first jar and see what happens.

The testing liquid is neither acid nor alkali. It contains a substance that changes when it is in contact with acids or alkalis. It turns red in an acid solution and a greenish-blue in alkali ones. What happened in your test?

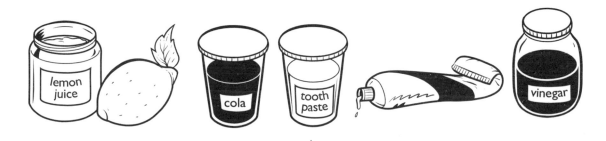

ROBOT INVASION

It's the year 2050 and robots are taking over the Earth. Solve the puzzles to defeat them, then turn to pages 63 and 64 to check your answers.

METAL MUNCH MIX-UP

This robot has been designed to help you fight robot enemies. He eats metal and needs feeding before he can help.

Can you complete the contents of his stomach so that each column, each row, and each of the four larger squares contains only one coat hanger, one fork, one phone and one saucepan?

DOGBOT ATTACK

a nasty dogbot

The dogbots are attacking! They are all run from a central computer, and to hack into it you will need to enter the password 7, 3, 9, 4 in 'binary code'. Binary code is the language that all computers use to process information.

The information is converted into ones (1) and zeros (0). Can you work out the sequence of ones and zeros you need to enter to stop the dogbots in their tracks?

DECIMAL	0	1	2	3	4	5	6	7	8	9	10
BINARY	0	1	10	11	100	101	110	111	1000	1001	1010

PARTS PANIC

Quick! You need to build a robot that will fight all the other robots before they break into the house.

Only one of these boxes contains all the parts you need to build the robot below. Can you work out which box it is?

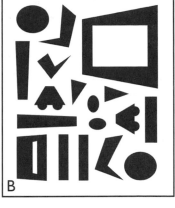

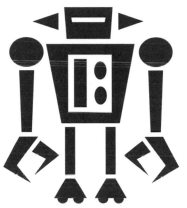

PROGRAMMER POWER

The letters opposite represent different types of robot. Each of the circles represents a robot power that has been programmed into its computer.

Where the circles cross over each other, the robots are programmed to do more than one thing. For example, robot J can walk forwards and shoot lasers, and robot D can walk backwards as well as sideways.

Can you spot the robot that can shoot lasers, walk sideways and forwards but can't walk backwards?

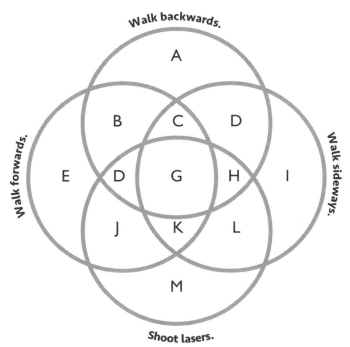

45

TIMED TABLE-TOP TEST

To take this table-top test you will need a wristwatch (with a second hand), a table, a coin and a mug. Use the second hand to time how long it takes you to complete all three parts of the test, then write your scores in the chart below. Then try to beat your own top time!

Before you begin, place the mug so that it is one hand span from the edge of the table, and place the coin so that it is touching the edge, as shown below. Now you are ready to begin the challenges.

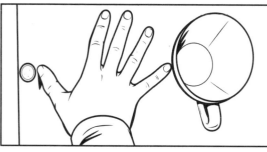

CHALLENGE 1

The aim of this challenge is to flick the coin around the mug until it is touching or hanging over the opposite edge of the table.

Use only your index finger to flick the coin. If you accidentally flick the coin off the table, start again. Don't push or drag the coin– that's cheating! You can use as many flicks as you like to complete the challenge.

CHALLENGE 2

This challenge takes skill and accuracy. First, spin the coin on its edge like so:

Then catch it between your thumbs before it falls, as shown here:

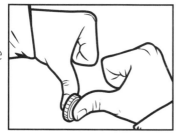

CHALLENGE 3

Still holding the coin between your thumbs, move your hands to the edge of the table by the mug.

Use your thumbs to throw the coin into the mug to complete the challenge.

SCORE CHART

Write your times in the chart below:

	Total Time
1st Attempt	
2nd Attempt	
3rd Attempt	

Design the ultimate water slide here.

REAL-LIFE HEROES

Get ready to be inspired by incredible true stories about brave and amazing boys all over the world.

HOOPS OF HOPE

When Austin Gutwein from Arizona, USA, was nine years old he saw a video about people dying of a disease called AIDS in Africa. He decided to use his passion for basketball to raise money to send to victims of AIDS and organized a sponsored 'hoop-a-thon' for World AIDS Day. He shot hoops all day and raised $3,000.

Determined to do more to help, Austin founded an organization named Hoops of Hope. Over 1,000 children are now members of it and have raised over $100,000.

Teaming up with the charity World Vision, they have helped provide millions of orphaned children with food, clothing and education.

MONEY MAKER

Bilaal Rajan from Toronto, Canada, is the National Child Representative for UNICEF (United Nations Children's Fund) in Canada and one of the charity's youngest ever fundraisers. When Bilaal was eight, a tsunami hit Southeast Asia, and he raised $50,000 all by himself to help the people whose homes and livelihoods had been destroyed.

Bilaal encouraged other children to do what they could for those affected, by visiting schools, creating his own website, and asking companies to help. The effort raised millions.

He has since visited Thailand, Indonesia, Sri Lanka and the Maldives to see how the money raised has helped affected communities.

RADIO STAR

When orphaned Baruani Ndume was seven ears old, he fled from war in the Democratic Republic of Congo in Africa and went to live in a refugee camp in another African country called Tanzania.

Thousands of refugees arrived at the camp, and many of the children had become separated from their families. Baruani has lived at the camp ever since and during this time he has created a radio programme called 'Children For Children' from very limited resources.

His radio show broadcasts programmes about the difficulties facing the children who live there, and helps to reunite children with their families. In 2009, he was awarded the International Children's Peace Prize.

EDUCATION DEFENDER

At the age of five, Om Prakash Gurjar was taken away from his parents and forced into slavery. He was rescued a few years later and given the opportunity to go to school.

Determined to protect other children from being forced into slavery and going through similar experiences, he has since fought successfully for free education for all children in a large area of India called Rajasthan.

He has met the President of India, and following a meeting in 2007 with Gordon Brown, the then British Prime Minister, was promised €300 million (about $400 million) in investment to provide education for the poorest children in the country.

PERISCOPE PUZZLER

You are part of an underwater mission to gain intelligence about
an evil genius called The Puzzler who has set up headquarters
on Jigsaw Island. You are in submarine 1 and took photograph C
of the island using a periscope – a device that lets you see above water.
Three other submarines have sent you their photos. Can you work out
which submarine took which photo of the island in order to identify
the exact location of each one before reporting back to base?
Check your answers on page 64.

You use your periscope to zoom in on a jigsaw The Puzzler is working on. Can you figure out which of the pieces are needed to complete the jigsaw? What does the completed puzzle tell you?

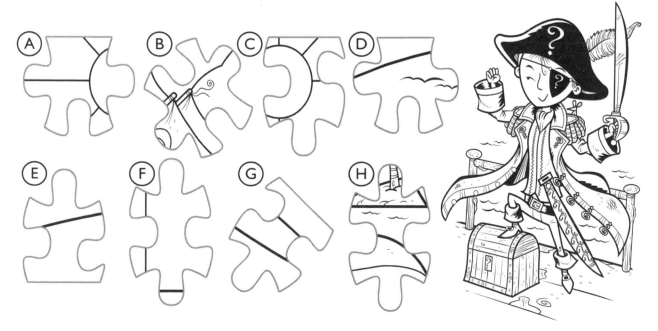

EXTREME ASSAULT COURSE

It's time to put yourself to the test with this extreme indoor assault course. Set up each of the activities below, then use a stopwatch to time how long it takes you to complete each challenge on the course.

CHALLENGE 1: BELLY CRAWL

Set up: Make a wall of cushions roughly 1 m (3 ft) in length, in front of a sofa.

Lay one end of a large sheet over the top of the wall of cushions and tuck the other end between the sofa cushions and the sofa to create a tunnel, as shown here.

Challenge: Lie on your belly and crawl through the tunnel as fast as you can.

CHALLENGE 2: CHAIR LASERS

Set up: Place four chairs in a row, spaced 1 m (3 ft) apart. Take a piece of string and tie it from the back-left leg of the front chair to the front-left leg of the back chair. Do the same on the right-hand side.

Challenge: The strings represent laser beams that you mustn't touch. Your mission is to zigzag between all of the chairs, stepping over the lasers. If you touch a beam, you must go back to the beginning and start again.

CHALLENGE 3: SINKING SAND

Set up: Lay a large sheet on the floor. The sheet represents an area of sinking sand. Find two pieces of A4 (8½ x 11 in) paper.

Challenge: Use the pieces of paper as stepping stones to cross the sinking sand as quickly as you can. To do this, each time you take a step, you will need to pick up the piece of paper behind you and move it forward to take the next step.

CHALLENGE 4: CAVE CHALLENGE

Set up: Blow up lots of balloons and tie them to lengths of string. Use sticky tape to hang the balloons down from the underside of a table so that they are nearly reaching the floor. (If you don't have any balloons you could use strips of newspaper.)

Challenge: To complete this challenge, crouch down and fight through the balloons as you run under the table and out the other end.

CHALLENGE 5: CRABWALK

Set up: Tape a piece of string or ribbon across a doorway to make a finish line.

Challenge: Crabwalk from the cave challenge to the finish line. To do this, sit on the floor with your knees bent and lean back on your hands. Lift your bottom off the ground and crabwalk sideways as fast as you can.

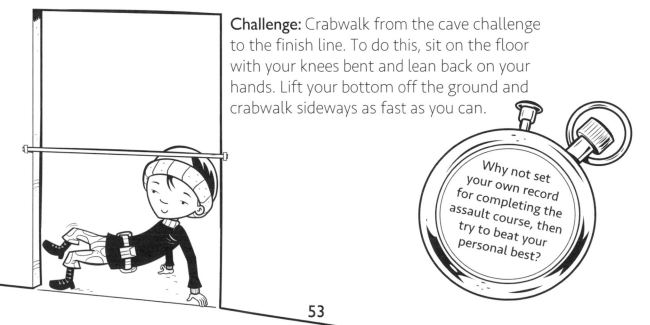

Why not set your own record for completing the assault course, then try to beat your personal best?

GALACTIC CARPET CROQUET

There's an asteroid heading to Earth that will destroy the planet. The only hope is to launch a missile that will blow up the asteroid before it enters our solar system. You are on a spaceship that is perfectly placed to launch the missile. You have been sent the instructions below to create four space gateways from items found on your craft. Can you guide the missile through the space gateways and blow up the asteroid in time?

You will need to find the following on your spaceship:

- foil • 8 yogurt pots • a golf ball
- a long cardboard tube (for example, from the middle of the roll of foil).

1. To make the space gateways, tear off four 30 cm (12 in) wide strips of foil.

2. Roughly roll them lengthways so that you have four long, sturdy strips.

3. Carefully, use a pair of scissors to create a cross-shaped hole in the bottom of each of the yogurt pots, as shown here.

4. Push one end of a foil strip through the hole in one of the yogurt pots, then bend the strip to create an arch and push the other end through the hole in another pot. This is a space gateway. Make another three gateways in the same way.

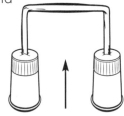
Space gateway.

5. Set the four space gateways up in a large square on the floor. Screw up a ball of foil – this is the asteroid – and place it in the middle of the square.

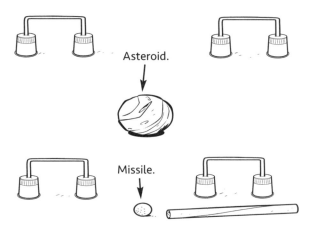
Asteroid.

Missile.

MISSILE LAUNCH

It is now time to launch the missile. Take the cardboard tube and hit the golf ball through each of the space gateways, then try to hit the asteroid in the middle to blow it up and save the day!

Why not time yourself to see how quickly you can do it, then try to beat your best score, or invite friends to play with you and see who can blow up the asteroid first?

RAINFOREST CHALLENGE

A rainforest tribe has invited you to take part in their annual challenge. If you successfully complete the challenge, you will be entitled to paint your face in the tribal pattern opposite:

Complete the grid so that the nine different pictures shown at the bottom of the page appear in every row, every column and in each outlined block of nine squares. The answer is on page 64.

MAKE A SPYSCOPE

Periscopes are special devices used by spies to spy around corners without being seen. Tanks and submarines are also fitted with periscopes to enable those inside to see what is around or above them. Find out how to make your own, then use it to spy on your family without being seen.

You will need:

- 2 clean, dry cardboard juice cartons
- a marker pen • scissors
- a ruler • strong tape • 2 small rectangular-shaped mirrors
- sticky tape.

1. Carefully cut the top off each juice carton.

2. Cut a rectangular shape out of the bottom of a carton, leaving roughly a 1 cm (¼ in) edge around the sides and bottom of the shape, as shown below.

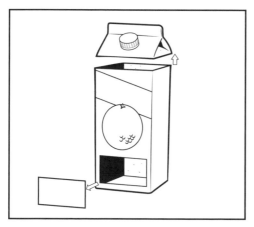

3. Place the carton on its side with the hole facing you. Lay a mirror flat on top of the carton so that its shorter side lines up with the base of the carton.

4. Mark a spot on the carton at the top right-hand and bottom left-hand corners of the mirror with a pen.

5. Remove the mirror and use your ruler to draw a diagonal line between the two dots, as shown.

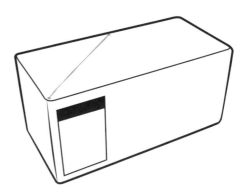

6. Carefully cut along the diagonal line you have drawn.

7. Slide the mirror through the slot that you have made.

8. Turn the carton round and look through the rectangular-shaped hole in the front of the carton.

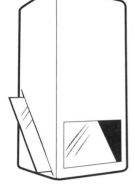

You should be able to see the top of the carton in the mirror.

9. Fix the mirror in place using tape.

10. Repeat steps **2** to **9** with the other carton.

11. Turn one of the cartons upside down and place it on top of the other one.

Make sure a rectangular-shaped opening is at the bottom of one carton facing you and the other opening is

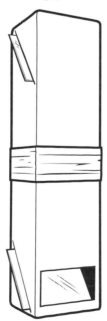

at the top of the other one and facing away from you.

12. Position the cartons so that when you look through the bottom opening, you can see what is ahead of you.

13. Fix the two cartons together with tape, as shown here.

YOUR SPYSCOPE MISSION

Hold your spyscope horizontally to look around corners, or hold it vertically to look over walls and fences.

You will find that what is ahead of you is reflected in the upper mirror, and then reflected in the lower mirror.

Your Mission: Not to be seen.

Time how long you can observe people around you without them seeing you.

If you get spotted, start the clock again. Make notes on what your targets are doing while you spy on them.

COLOSSEUM CONUNDRUMS

You're going to have to fight for your life to solve these puzzles! The answers are on page 64.

THIEF!

There is a thief somewhere in the crowd who has a beard, is wearing a brooch and doesn't have a laurel wreath headdress. Can you spot him?

STATUE SPOTS

Can you spot ten differences between the statues of the Roman Emperor on the opposite page?

DID YOU KNOW?

The Colosseum was the name of the biggest games arena in Rome. It could seat up to 50,000 people. In the arena, many prisoners were forced to fight gladiators – men who were trained in deadly fighting techniques at special schools.

Give the gladiators swords and decorate their shields.

LOOK BEHIND YOU ...

Gladiators were forced to fight wild beasts, including wolves, bears and large cats. Join the dots below to see what's behind the gladiator in time to warn him. Quick, before it's too late!

DESIGN YOUR OWN DINO COMIC STRIP

Learn how to draw Toby the T-Rex, then make him the star of your own comic-book adventures.

To draw Toby, follow the instructions below. Try drawing him on rough paper before starring him in the comic strips opposite.

You will need:

• rough paper • a pencil • a black pen • an eraser • some felt-tip pens.

1. Use a pencil to draw rough ovals to show Toby's head and body. Add two lines coming to a point for his tail.

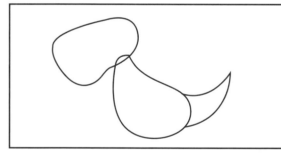

2. Add lines for his arms, legs and feet, copying the shapes shown below as closely as you can.

3. Draw an 'M' shape for Toby's eyes, then draw his mouth and claws in pencil. Go over your final lines with the black pen.

4. Draw in triangles for his teeth and circles for his eyeballs. Wait for the pen to dry, then erase all the pencil lines. Use the felt-tip pens to complete your picture of Toby.

Now you have drawn Toby the T-Rex, make him feature in your very own dino comic strip on the opposite page. Will he escape the nasty dinosaur and live to tell the tale?

THE ADVENTURES OF TOBY THE T-REX

WHAT HAPPENS NEXT? YOU DECIDE!

ALL THE ANSWERS

RIDE ON
pages 6 and 7

A. 4 skaters have backpacks on.
B. 5 skaters are completely in the air.
C. 3 skaters have one arm in the air and have both feet on their skateboards.
D. 3 skaters have crash-landed.

Jim would have to land on this square marked with a cross:

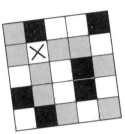

Skater **1**'s wallet is:

Skater **2**'s wallet is:

Skater **3**'s wallet is:

Skater **4**'s wallet is:

MISSION: SECRET AGENT
pages 8 and 9

Agent's Code Name: Agent Rainstorm.

UNBELIEVABLE WEATHER
page 12

FACT 8 is false. All snow crystals are hexagonal (this means they have six sides) but no two snow crystals have ever been found to be identical.

MOUNTAIN OF DOOM
page 15

SPORTS-QUIZ SHOWDOWN
pages 18 and 19

1. Rowing, boxing, weightlifting and football are Olympic sports. The others are not.

2. Camel– Wrestling (Turkey)
Bull – Running (Spain)
Duck – Derby (USA)
Hot Dog – Eating (USA)
Elephant – Polo (Nepal)

3. Love, Deuce – Tennis
Salute, Parry – Fencing
Birdie, Eagle – Golf
Skittle, Strike – Ten-Pin bowling
Duck, Boundary – Cricket

4. B, **5.** C – caught, bowled, leg before wicket, stumped, run out, hit wicket, handled the ball, obstructed the field, hit the ball twice, timed out, **6.** A, **7.** A, **8.** D, **9.** B.

CAN YOU SAVE THE DAY?
pages 22 and 23

The Ugly Crew ended up in house **B**.

The code for the safe is:
Nasty Nemesis: 14, 1, 19, 20, 25 /
14, 5, 13, 5, 19, 9, 19

The gold is 'buried under tree,
next to hospital'.

Goblin Gordon's print was
found on the gold.

The robbers' prison numbers are in the
following squares; **A5**, **D5** and **G4**.

GO-KART GO!
page 29

FLY TRAP
page 32

Spider **1** has trapped fly **C**.
Spider **2** has trapped fly **D**.
Spider **3** has trapped fly **B**.
Spider **4** has trapped fly **A**.

RAIN-DANCE DIFFERENCES
page 33

SAFARI SPOT
page 38

Giraffe	3	Rhino	5
Lion	3	Zebra	5
Cheetah	2	Elephant	2
	Warthog	3	

ROBOT INVASION
pages 44 and 45

The code is: 111, 11, 1001, 100

Box C contains all the pieces needed to make the robot.

Robot K can shoot lasers, walk forwards and sideways but can't walk backwards.

PERISCOPE PUZZLER
pages 50 and 51

Submarine **2** took picture **D**.
Submarine **3** took picture **A**.
Submarine **4** took picture **B**.

A, **B**, **E** and **H** are the missing jigsaw pieces.

The Puzzler's pirate ship is coming towards the submarine, which tells you that you need to make a quick getaway!

RAINFOREST CHALLENGE
page 55

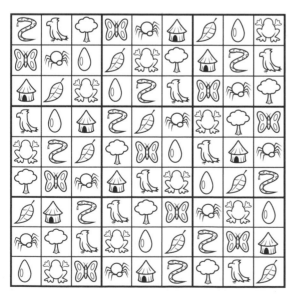

COLOSSEUM CONUNDRUMS
pages 58 and 59

The thief is standing up in the first row on the right-hand page, as shown here:

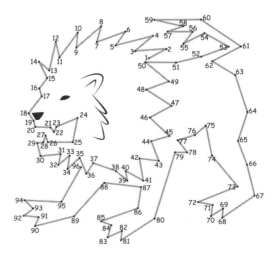